First published 1999

ISBN 0 7110 2638 6

© Hinton J. Sheryn 1999

Published by Ian Allan Publishing

an imprint of Ian Allan Publishing Ltd,
Terminal House, Shepperton, Surrey
TW17 8AS.
Printed by Ian Allan Printing Ltd, Riverdene
Business Park, Hersham, Surrey KT12 4RG.

Code: 9905/C3

Heavy Plant IN COLOUR

Hinton J. Sheryn

Front cover: The Demag-
Komatsu hydraulic front shovel
is the largest in the company's
range of heavy-duty mining
excavators. The previous largest
was the model H485SP, which
weighed in at 685 tons carrying
a 46cu yd bucket. The H655S
will obviously top these
specifications substantially.
Mannesmann Demag Ltd

Back cover: The Bucyrus 495-B
at a coal mine in Colorado.

Right: The Caterpillar 5130
hydraulic face-shovel and 785B
dump truck at work for Wimpey
Mining in the South Wales
coalfield in 1994.
*Courtesy of Finning (UK) Ltd
(Marcus Pitt) & Caterpillar Inc.*

Ian Allan
PUBLISHING

Contents

Right:
A Liebherr A900 Litronic wheeled excavator delivered to the Witham Third District Internal Drainage Board and used to clean canals, rivers and waterways with its double dipper arm and a specially adapted bucket.
Liebherr GB Ltd

Picture Credits:
All uncredited pictures are from the author's collection.

Introduction

The emergence of the steam engine was the late 19th century's biggest single revolution in the mechanisation of mass excavation and earthmoving. The steam engine was used to power hundreds of shovels and draglines which dug hundreds of miles of canals, railways and dams all over the world. Bucket-ladder dredgers cut batters along canal banks from the Suez Canal in Egypt to the Panama Canal in Central America.

Steam also powered cranes equipped with grab buckets for excavation and handling of materials including coal, iron-ore, clays and stone. Few steam-powered bulldozers or scrapers were to emerge, as by the beginning of the 20th century the internal combustion engine (petrol, gas, paraffin or diesel) had been successfully adapted for use on tractors. Many thousands of steam traction engines and steamrollers were used for a variety of haulage, agricultural and timber applications, but few were adapted for earthmoving.

Rope operation of the excavator, scraper, wheel and tracked loader, and bulldozer reigned supreme for the first 50 years of the 20th century. Outclassing all previous inventions, the advent of high-pressure hydraulics has totally transformed all aspects of excavating, earthmoving and material handling.

By the millennium, the first hydraulic excavator to reach the 1,000-ton mark will almost certainly be with us. In 1998/9, machines are in the 600- to 800-ton arena. Bucket capacities of around 50cu yd are commonplace in products from at least seven major manufacturers of large mining-size hydraulic excavators.

Massive crawler-mounted and wheel (truck)-mounted mobile cranes are now constructed to lift loads from 250 to 1,600 tons: they use hydraulics to power the heavy-duty winches or to raise the huge booms, and in many cases to provide total telescopic action of booms, extending them to amazingly long proportions.

Hydraulics are frequently being used to break concrete and rock with high-powered breakers. Heavy-gauge steel is cut with shears like carrots on major demolition projects.

Trenches are being dug, not just along the pavement or roadway with hydraulic excavators of the wheel digger loader type, mini or midi fully-slewing diggers or large swing shovels, but also with endless-chain trenchers, which range from small pedestrian-operated machines to massive trenchers capable of cutting deep trenches across whole countries for the installation of water, gas and oil pipelines.

Dump-trucks are in use around the world which rely on hydraulics for steering and dumping a load: they have capacities from just a few tons to well over 300 tons.

Bulldozer blades are raised and lowered under hydraulic pressure as well as angled and tilted in all directions. Many of the track-mounted machines also feature hydraulic-operated rippers: the very large machines can penetrate a depth of several feet, enabling them to remove very hard rock which would otherwise require blasting. Where blasting is necessary to loosen vast volumes of overburden in surface mines, or in large quarries for the loosening or fracturing of rock, large purpose-built drills are used. They rely heavily on hydraulics to provide the angle of the mast and to raise or lower the borer and rotate the drill itself.

Only on the very large electrically-powered cable-operated mining shovels and walking draglines are hydraulics relatively unimportant. In Russia, however, unlike the vast majority of American draglines, hydraulics are widely used to operate the walking mechanisms. Only *Big-Muskie* (the Bucyrus-Erie 4250-W, a 14,000-ton American-designed and built walking-dragline) did use huge hydraulic cylinders to push and lift the massive shoes which enabled it to walk. All other American- and British-made machines used eccentric-cam methods.

However large the recently developed hydraulic excavators have become, they will remain very small compared with the 'Super' shovels of the 1950s and 1960s: then mammoth machines, weighing from around 3,000 tons to 14,000 tons, gouged huge tracts of land in North America to recover shallow coal deposits. Standing as high as 22- or even 24-storey buildings and with swinging buckets to 180cu yd capacity, they were impressive by any standard. Sadly, these huge machines have almost all been cut up for scrap. One or two have been preserved as monuments to the era,

and a few are still completing their work in United States coal mines, often after 30 or more years of continuous overburden removal.

Walking-draglines in the 4,000- to 9,000-ton classes are still being ordered from the American manufacturers. Russian manufacturers of large walking draglines still receive regular orders from the coal and mineral mines of the CIS nations.

German, Austrian and Polish makes of huge bucket-wheel excavators are still being requested for work in the lignite and brown coal mines of Eastern Europe. The largest of these machines, weighing in excess of 14,500 tons, are capable of excavating as much as 240,000 tons of material in just one day. One such mine now has no less than six such machines with another on order for commissioning in 1999.

From a small hole in a pavement to the removal of a mountain — both are feasible with an excavator of one sort or another. Bulldozers, trenchers and other machines are also working regularly on the seabeds of our world's oceans.

Acknowledgements

Among the many who have helped with this book are the following companies and individuals who have kindly allowed use of photographs and other material:

Hydraulic Excavators
O&K, Liebherr, Demag-Komatsu, Finning (UK) Ltd.

Shovels and Draglines
Marion Power Shovel Co, Harnischfeger Corporation (P&H), Bucyrus International, Uralmash, Jim Rosso, Fording Coal Ltd.

Bucket-wheel Excavators
Poltegor Engineering, KWK, Voest-Alpine, Krupp Fordertechnik, Siemens.

Dump Trucks
Unit Rig, Terex, DDT, Bell, Heathfield-Haulmatic, Liebherr, Komatsu Mining Systems Inc.

Bulldozers, Loaders and Graders
Tiger Engineering, Komatsu, Caterpillar, Finning (UK) Ltd, VME/Graham Miller, Royal Engineers' Library, Chatham.

Trenchers
Burkeen (Andrew Chadleck), Wesley Moore (Alfred J. Moore & Sons Ltd), Mr Marcel De Jong (Mastenbroek), Trencor.

Ancillary Equipment
Bucyrus International.

Cranes
Tadano-Faun, SMC, Komatsu, Demag, Manitowoc, Mammoet, Walter-Wright Mammoet, Mark Evans (Mannesmann Dematic), Ainscough Crane Hire Ltd (Lorraine and Danielle in particular).

I am also very grateful to Mrs Sharon Rees (Home Office) for her work on the manuscript.

Hydraulic Excavators

Right: A wheel-mounted Komatsu PW170 hydraulic backhoe excavator equipped with a rotating dipper handle, enabling the bucket to operate in various directions and offer total versatility. *Marubeni-Komatsu*

Left: An O&K MH5 wheel-mounted excavator is here equipped with a hydraulic grab. This machine can operate under its own power along railway lines and so make speedy repairs with minimal assistance from personnel other than the operator. *Sandhurst Plant*

Right: This O&K MH4 PMS111 is a 13.5-tonne wheel-mounted excavator, powered by a 58kW engine. It has a bucket capacity of 0.7cu m in backhoe configuration. *Sandhurst Plant*

Far left: The Komatsu PW130-6 wheel-mounted excavator has an engine output of 84hp/62.5kW, weighs in at 14,290kg and has bucket capacities of 0.12-1.14cu m. *Marubeni-Komatsu*

Below: This Liebherr hydraulic excavator is equipped with a demolition sheer, capable of crunching through steel as we would crunch into an apple. *Liebherr GB Ltd*

Left: A Liebherr 984 crawler excavator equipped with high reach demolition boom and a long dipper arm. *Liebherr GB Ltd*

Left: A Komatsu PC400LC ripping away at a building in Berlin. *Marubeni-Komatsu*

Below: A Liebherr 974 equipped with long reach boom, dipper stick and scrap-handling 'orange-peel' grab. *Liebherr GB Ltd*

This Liebherr 984 hydraulic scrap-handling excavator is not only equipped with long reach booms and orange-peel grab, but also a high-level operator's cab, enabling the operator to load this huge ship safely. *Liebherr GB Ltd*

Left: This 38-tonne O&K RH16 crawler excavator is mounted on heavy-duty tracks which will enable it to dig in the toughest conditions and handle large tonnages with ease. *Sandhurst Plant*

Above: This O&K RH City is loading gravel using a grading-type bucket (it has no teeth attached to it). As for all modern-day excavators, a wide range of sizes and types of buckets is available, some for trench excavating (various widths), others for general excavating and others for handling light materials. Other options include hydraulic grabs, scabblers and a device which can make mincemeat of hard rock or concrete, in addition to the heavy-duty hammers also used to break up rock and concrete. *Sandhurst Plant*

Right: The RH-30 O&K-Terex, at 77 tonnes, is the largest excavator in the 'contractor' size range normally equipped with backacter. Larger machines would generally be equipped with front-shovel backacters (though they are optional equipment). *Terex-O&K*

Right: The O&K-Terex RH-120C equipped with front-loading bullclam weighs in at 234 tonnes. This is a truly mining-size excavator and one of the most popular in numbers sold worldwide since its introduction in 1983. *Terex-O&K*

Below: One of the more recent heavyweights to emerge from O&K-Terex was this model RH170 at 360 tonnes, already at work in many mines around the world. *Terex-O&K*

Right: Already hard at work in large mining operations in Canada is the giant RH400. At no less than 800 tonnes, it sports bucket capacities of 40-45cu m. The type is currently loading some of the largest dump trucks in the business, to recover valuable minerals. In this case, oil is being excavated from Syncrude's tar sands or oil shale. Two of these giant excavators work on this operation. *Terex-O&K*

Below: The Komatsu PC200EN excavator is in the 20-ton class. This new series of machines differs dramatically from the original Komatsus. Gone is the square appearance, with the redesigned, curved cab and superstructure. *Marubeni-Komatsu*

Right: The Komatsu PC1600 loading shot rock. Komatsu entered into an arrangement with Demag, the German manufacturer of heavy-duty quarrying and mining shovels, to jointly manufacture and market under the Demag-Komatsu name. Demag has been producing very large excavators very successfully for some years. The PC1600 was probably produced before the partnership. *Komatsu*

Below: The opencast coal contractor Clay Colliery Ltd is using a Liebherr 984 fitted with backacter to remove overburden at this mine. *Liebherr GB Ltd/Clay Colliery Ltd*

Right: This O&K RH15 dates from the mid-1980s, and is fitted with a front shovel. *O&K*

Left: NSM, one of the large opencast mining contractors, is here using an O&K RH75 to load overburden in the late 1980s/early '90s. The company was once owner and operator of an O&K RH300, which, although a very large excavator, proved unsuccessful. Other O&K machines have not met with such problems. *O&K*

Below: A Demag H65 front-shovel handling an oversize rock with ease in this quarry. *Demag-Komatsu*

Above: A Demag H95 with bullclam front-shovel loading a Euclid R-50 rear dump truck. Note the narrow-gauge-track shoes, ideal for quarry work. *Mannesmann-Demag Ltd*

Left: The Demag model H135S with, in this case, a front shovel/bullclam attachment, is the start of something big from Demag. Although this is a very productive excavator for its size, there is more to come. *Mannesmann-Demag Ltd*

Right: The Demag H285S on this huge opencast mining project is able to load the dump-truck in just three or four passes, using its bullclam bucket. *Mannesmann-Demag Ltd*

Left: For several years the heaviest hydraulic excavator from Demag, with many of this model working around the world in large scale mining projects, such as this in the Pinto Valley, loading a massive Haulpak truck, the 485S. *Mannesmann-Demag Ltd*

Below: The Demag-Komatsu H685SP is an awesome excavator of dramatic proportions and immense power, handling thousands of tons overburden daily. *Mannesmann-Demag Ltd*

An interesting use of a Liebherr P994, pontoon-mounted for dredging duty in San Francisco. *Liebherr-Hydraulikbagger GMBH*

Shovels and Draglines —
Crawlers

Right: A 15cu yd Manitowoc crawler-mounted dragline.

Below: Quarrying for Fairclough Mining (part of the AMEC group) in the UK, a Marion 182-M.

Right: A crawler-mounted Lima 2400-B.

Below: 195-B electric shovel.

Right: Marion 184-M crawler dragline.

Left: Working on coal extraction in western Canada, a crawler-mounted Bucyrus 395-B.

Below: At Fording Coal's Mildred Lake tar-sands operation in northern Canada, several Marion 301-M shovels load 240-ton dump trucks in just three passes, using 85-ton payload buckets. This machine started work in these harsh conditions in 1991. *Fording Coal Ltd*

Below: From the huge Uralmash Co of Russia, this is one of hundreds of walking draglines it produced with electric shovels and hydraulic excavators. The model EW65.100 has a 65cu m bucket on 100m boom, and weighs 5,460 tons. Unlike almost all American draglines, Uralmash machines incorporated a fully hydraulic walking mechanism, using vertical rams to lift the machine and horizontal rams to perfect the walk. Many of these machines have seen service counted in decades rather than years: still, however, the requirement for more coal, iron-ore, phosphate, gold, diamonds and other minerals will ensure steady orders for these mammoth machines for many years to come.

Uralmash also produces the model EW100.125 which can operate buckets of 100cu m on 125cu m booms and has an operating weight of 10,000 tons. After Bucyrus-Erie's *Big-Muskie* (at 14,000 tons, the largest mobile land machine ever when it started work in 1969), the EW100.125 is clearly the second largest dragline in the world. Other less heavy walking draglines from Bucyrus and Marion have operated much larger buckets, however: 176 and 180cu yd on a number of their larger models, with many above 100cu yd. *Uralmash*

Right: The *Ace of Spades*, which operates at the Stobswood opencast coal site in Northumberland. It is a Pawling & Harnischfeger (P&H) 757, currently the largest dragline in Western Europe, at 4,417 tonnes, with a bucket of 65cu yd on a 310ft boom. (It is capable of operating buckets to 75cu yd.) Commissioned in December 1991, it started work full-time in February 1992. It walked over a mile from where it was erected to begin uncovering the vast deposits of coal in this mine.

The Harnischfeger Corporation (owner of the P&H logo) bought the Page Engineering Co in 1987. Page was one of the pioneers in dragline development and had over many years produced a comprehensive range of diesel and electric-powered machines which worked on phosphate, coal, potash and irrigation projects throughout the United States and Canada, Turkey and elsewhere.

Now that Marion has become part of Bucyrus International, P&H is left to become a major player in the walking dragline business, as is evident from orders being received from coal mines in Australia. *P&H-Harnischfeger Corporation*

Shovels and Draglines — Walking

Below: The Bulga mine in Australia was the purchaser of the largest P&H walking dragline by 1998. The '9020', named locally as the *Big Kahuna*, cost around 45 million dollars and is uncovering the rich bituminous coal fields of the Hunter Valley in New South Wales. Weighing 5,700 tons (about as heavy as 15 Jumbo Jets), its 320ft boom is longer than a football field: the boom tip towers 22 storeys above the ground, and the massive bucket has a capacity of 115cu yd (88cu m). It has a power rating of 27,970hp. It consumes around 4,900,000kW hours of electricity a month, enough to meet the requirements of a city of 10,000 homes. The large machine was unveiled early in 1996. A new, even larger dragline ordered for Australia's coal fields is likely to be in operation in 1999. *P&H-Harnischfeger Corporation.*

Right: A Bucyrus 2570WS walking dragline at work for the Thunder Basin Coal Co at Wright, Wyoming in the Powder River Basin, USA. *Bucyrus International*

Left: Seen in action in Louisiana, USA, a Bucyrus walking dragline.

Below: One of several very large walking draglines at work for Fording Coal at the Mildred Lake oil sands operation, northern Canada. The first Marion 8750-M went to work in the early 1990s, equipped with an 80cu yd bucket and 360ft boom. This 8750-M is a brand new machine. *Fording Coal Ltd*

Bucket-wheel Excavators

Below: The VABE-1500 bucket-wheel excavator from Voest Alpine Bergtechnik of Austria is an ultra-modern machine currently at work in locations around the world. *Voest Alpine Bergtechnik*

Right: The extremely large KWK-1500s working in a Polish lignite field. Note the onboard cranes used to assist with repairs and parts replacement. *KWK*

Above: Siemens in conjunction with O&K (both German companies) built the massive No 292 bucket-wheel excavator, which weighs in at 13,000 tons. It has a capacity of 240,000cu m/day, stands twice the height of New York's Statue of Liberty, and is as long as two and a half soccer pitches.

No 293 has been ordered for work in the Rheinbraun lignite field, with a bucket wheel diameter of 21.6m and a total of 18 buckets, each of 6.6cu m capacity. Discharge rate for the buckets is between 48 and 72 per min. There are currently seven machines in the 200,000cu m/day class. In 1976 two were commissioned by Siemens at the Fortuna open cut mine. Six were planned,

produced and assembled by Siemens, and to date the company has provided electrical equipment for more than 150 bucket-wheel excavators. It also provides electrical power equipment for draglines and shovels. *Siemens*

Right: Krupp Fördertechnik has been making endless-bucket excavators for over 120 years. Those working at the Hamback open-pit mine of Rheinbraun AG, Germany, include this giant. With a capacity of 240,000cu m/day, it was commissioned in 1978 to remove overburden and brown coal. *Krupp Fordertechnik*

A view from the work end of the giant Krupp bucket-wheel excavator which weighs in at 13,500 tons. *Krupp Industrietechnik*

Dump Trucks

A Terex dump truck at work on a British opencast coal site in the livery of Fairclough Mining, part of the AMEC group of companies.
AMEC Mining

Below: Many commentators have suggested that Scandinavian manufacturers such as BM-Volvo and Nord-Verk perfected the ADT or Articulated Dump Truck: they, with others, have certainly introduced many thousands of ADTs to the earthmoving industry since the 1960s. Much earlier, such companies as Le Tourneau-Westinghouse, Caterpillar, Allis-Chalmers, Curtiss-Wright and Michigan had all made dumper bodies available for two-wheel tractors which would otherwise have to be used in conjunction with scrapers.

Nevertheless, purpose-built ADTs have taken the industry by storm from all quarters, having the advantage of four- or six-wheel drive and fast turnaround as well as increasing payloads. Often companies manufacturing ADTs also offer rigid dump trucks as an alternative or for much heavier loads.

Heathfield and Haulamatic were two dump truck manufacturers who joined forces to market rigids and ADTs. The H50 Heathfield being loaded by a Liebherr 984 backhoe excavator on this excavation is becoming widely accepted as a formidable rugged dump-truck, well able to match any similar size truck on the market. The Heathfield was originally built at a factory near Newton Abbot in Devon, England, and named after a nearby village associated with clay mining. The company was absorbed by another manufacturer and production moved to the Midlands.
Bell Equipment Co

Left: The Bell ADT originates from South Africa and, with Heathfield-Haulamatic handling sales in Britain and Europe, it is quickly becoming a very popular choice on construction, quarry and mine sites there, as in its native country. This one, being loaded by a Liebherr 974 excavator, is no stranger to the steep grades and rugged terrain surrounding it — the B40B, in the 40-ton class, is doing work which would only have been practical with a rigid truck of that capacity a few years ago.
Bell Equipment Co

Right: The more recent upgraded Bell B25C series ADT. Becoming widely accepted in Europe as state-of-the-art workhorses, machines such as these are more than ready for the 21st century.
Bell Equipment Co

Left: The DDT 625B seen here was the first to be made, in 1997. The English company DDT offers two methods for unloading: the conventional hydraulic tip arrangement, or the unique horizontal displacement for which the company has a patent. This uses an ejector system similar to that employed by scrapers, though in this case the contents are removed from the dumper over the tail of the unit by a large ejector plate operated by hydraulic rams. It can, therefore, empty 'on the move' and eliminate the possibility of the body tipping over when the butt is full in the air, a common occurrence with such dumpers when operating on rough tipping areas. *DDT Engineering Ltd*

Left: Dump trucks with carrying capacities of 340 tons are now commonplace in some of the largest mining projects in Canada, North and South America, Australia and elsewhere — hence the need for the extremely large electric cable shovels, hydraulic excavators and mammoth wheel-loaders to keep loading time to a bare minimum.

Seen being loaded by a mighty Bucyrus International electric mining shovel, the MT-4400 Lectra-Haul is a product of Unit-Rig (now part of the Terex Corporation, which also owns the construction equipment/excavator manufacturer O&K). Built in Tulsa, Oklahoma, these dump-trucks are rated at 260 tons (236

tonnes). With maximum gross weight of 865,000lb (392,300kg), they are powered by a Cummins K2000E diesel of 2,000hp SAE (1,492kW) or an MTU 16V 396 TE of 2,467hp (1,840 kW). Height in tip position is 41ft 11in, length is 45ft 7in and width 24ft 2in.
Terex Corporation

Below:
A P&H/Kobelco electric mining shovel empties its huge dipper into a Lectra-Haul MT-4400 truck at this vast coal mine.
Terex Corporation

Left: At Warkworth Mining Ltd's vast coal mine in Australia, nine T-262 Liebherr trucks, fitted with MTU engines, are hard at work. Two began operation from October 1994, and the remaining seven were shipped from the United States factory between November 1995 and August 1996. *Liebherr Mining Trucks Inc*

Below: Thunder Basin Coal Co at Wright in the Powder River Basin, Wyoming, USA, operates no less than 14 of these massive trucks around the clock to recover vast coal deposits. Again, the T-262

Liebherr is proving its worth in heavy mining conditions. The large P&H electric shovel is loading coal direct from the seam into the truck. The T-262 (formerly known as the KL-2450) is rated at 240-ton-plus capacity, engine output 2,000-2,500hp and was first built by Wiseda (later acquired by Liebherr) at Baxter Springs, Kansas. The 298-ton T-272 and 340-ton T-282 are planned for full production in 1999. The Black Thunder mine purchased its first KL-2450 in 1986. *Liebherr Mining Trucks Inc*

Right: A rugged Terex 3360 rear dump truck is a hardworking machine by any standards, never better than with a hefty 60 tons of rock on board. *Terex*

Left: The Terex 2566C ADT, a 25-ton-capacity truck whose six-wheel drive enables it to negotiate the roughest conditions with ease. *Terex*

Right: Being loaded by an O&K front-shovel hydraulic excavator is this Terex 4066C articulated dump truck. Terex, whose manufacturing plant is at Motherwell in Scotland, has recently acquired O&K. *Terex-O&K*

Left: Two Komatsu 830E, 255-ton-capacity dump trucks being loaded by a massive Bucyrus electric mining shovel at this large American mine. The Komatsu Haulpak range of dump trucks has an interesting pedigree: the company which introduced it in 1957 began in the early 1900s as R. G. Le Tourneau, and was succeeded by Le Tourneau-Westinghouse, WABCO (Westinghouse Air Brake Co), Dresser Construction & Mining Equipment Co, Komatsu-Dresser, and finally Komatsu Mining Systems Inc.
Komatsu Mining Systems Inc

Below: The Komatsu 930E is rated at 320-ton capacity — almost 100 of these huge trucks were operating in mines around the world in 1998. Powered by a 2,700hp MTU/DDC 16V 4000 engine, it is 50ft long, 27ft 8in wide, and 23ft 10in high. Komatsu and other manufacturers of very large dump trucks are already looking to a 360-ton capacity.
Komatsu Mining Systems Inc

Bulldozers, Loaders and Graders

Left: The world's largest bulldozer is the D575A from Komatsu, weighing in at 314,200lb (142,500kg), with a blade capacity of 90cu yd (69cu m). It has a Komatsu SA12V170 engine developing 1,150hp (888kW). Two of these super-dozers are seen at this mine site. *Komatsu Mining Systems Inc*

Below: Not many of these around now, but for many years the Fowler Challenger 33 crawler bulldozer was to be found in abundance on coal tips at power stations, landfill sites, quarries and earthmoving projects, with just its blade, or towing cable-operated scrapers. It was made in Leeds, Yorkshire by the company that made hundreds of traction engines and steamrollers prior to the onslaught of the internal-combustion engine.

Left: Made by Tiger Engineering in Australia and first released in 1981, the Tiger Dozer is based on the Caterpillar 992 Loader, and is familiar on large-scale mining projects in Canada, the United States and Australia. This large wheel-bulldozer is ideally suited to levelling spoil/overburden dumps and cleaning up around excavators at the face of opencast mines.

In 1998, the Tiger range was absorbed by Caterpillar International which has now added these models to its portfolio.

Caterpillar components used include the 773B (dump truck) lock-up torque converter with advanced electronic control, and a single-lever blade control. It uses the Caterpillar D10N hydraulic system including twin-blade lift cylinders, and the 'Stic' control system (multi-function control with steering and transmission integrated into one controller). Blade capacities range from 24.4cu yd for a semi-V to 50cu yd for a coal blade. Gross power is 548kW/736hp.

Other models in the Tiger range include 590hp and 800hp versions and a blade capacity of 30cu yd for semi-V blade and 60cu yd for the coal blade.
Courtesy of Caterpillar Inc & Tiger Engineering

Right:
The Caterpillar 992G wheel loader is the largest CAT model currently popular at mines and quarries in the United Kingdom: the even larger 994 is achieving high production targets at sites in Australia, North and South America and Canada. The 992G does, however, include features such as the patented 'Stic' control which leaves the operator's right hand free to control the bucket. The 992G in this photograph is loading a CAT 777D dump truck at the Hillhead quarry near Buxton in Derbyshire.
Courtesy of Finning (UK) Ltd (Marcus Pitt) & Caterpillar Inc

Left: Komatsu's largest wheel loader, the WA900 of 853hp (636kW), has a 17cu yd (13cu m) capacity (or 15cu yd as a high-lift shovel). The company has announced its intention to design a much larger machine to rival the mighty Le Tourneau L-1800 and Caterpillar 994.
Komatsu Mining Systems Inc

Right: Volvo and Euclid have been working partners for a number of years — Volvo of Sweden has long been producing one of the world's most popular ranges of wheel loaders, along with its famed ADT dump trucks, and, more recently, rigid-frame dumpers. Euclid, one of America's earthmoving pioneers, has long been famous for rear dump trucks. An articulated, steer-all hydraulic wheel loader from Volvo is loading one of the latest Euclid rear dump trucks in this quarry.
VME/Graham Miller

Left: Motor graders such as this Komatsu GD825A-2 are an essential part of all mining operations: clearing haul roads; cutting drainage ditches; ripping; and cleaning up around loading shovels. This is a 280hp (209kW) machine powered by a Komatsu SGD140E diesel engine. It has a 16ft 2in-long blade, and, with a rear-mounted ripper, the machine is 37ft 8in long. *Komatsu Mining Systems Inc*

Below: An Aveling-Barford six-wheel-drive, six-wheel-steer grader equipped with underslung grader blade and a front-mounted bulldozer blade. The machine is used by the Medway-based Royal Engineers in the UK. *Royal Engineers' Library, Chatham*

Trenchers

Below left: The B13 is one of Burkeen's small trenchers used mainly in the digging of trenches for water, gas or electricity pipes or cables. Rubber tyres minimise damage to the surroundings.
Burkeen Trencher Link (Mr Andrew Chladek)

Below right: The B36B from Burkeen combines a rear-mounted chain trencher, a front-mounted backacter hydraulic excavator and a bulldozer backfilling blade.
Burkeen Trencher Link (Mr Andrew Chladek)

This Steenbergen machine, made in Klaaswaal in the Netherlands, works for Alfred J Moore & Sons Ltd of Devon. The GSS300 Super was made in the 1960s or early 1970s, is able to cut trenches to 3m deep, and is powered by a 295hp engine.

Wesley Moore of A. J. Moore & Sons Ltd

Left: Similar to the Steenbergen machine is this Mastenbroek type 30/20, a 300hp drainage trencher. These machines are able to dig the trench and lay the pipe in one operation. *Mastenbroek*

Right: A Mastenbroek type 30/25 40-ton trencher working in roads and rock for this gas-pipe contract in Japan. The machine is powered by a 330hp engine and can dig 2.5m deep and 900mm wide. *Mastenbroek*

Left: Mastenbroek type SS50/55 sub-sea trencher weighing 60 tons. Working here on pipe installation, the 500hp machine can work in a maximum 100m depth of water, and has a digging depth of 5.5m and width of 800mm. *Mastenbroek*

A Mastenbroek type 17/17, 185hp, 18-ton, trencher on rock excavation work for a cable project in Amman, Jordan. *Mastenbroek*

Above: At 560hp, this 70-ton model 50/36 from Mastenbroek is working on drainage in the Syrian desert. Its digging depth is 4m and trench width 400mm. *Mastenbroek*

Right: Installing concrete pipes in Germany is this Mastenbroek type 50/36, 80-ton, 525hp trencher. *Mastenbroek*

Above: From Trencor of Grapevine, Texas, USA, the mighty 1860HD is one of the largest trenchers in the world. Weighing around 185 tons, it uses one 1,200hp engine to provide power for the digging chain and a further 300hp engine to power the tracks, conveyors and all other functions. It is able to dig to 35ft deep (10.6m) and when equipped with a Roadminer attachment, which replaces the normal digging assembly, it can dig 17ft wide and cut to 6ft deep in a single pass. The 1860HD has been used around the world on tough contracts including a massive gas pipeline from North Africa through Spain and Portugal. *Trencor*

Right: Good use was made of a Trencor 1860HD through the South Devon countryside, through granite and clays. The chain ladder is fitted with hundreds of carbide-tipped cutters enabling it to slice through most materials it meets with. *Trencor*

Ancillary Equipment

Inset: Air compressors have been an essential part of mining, quarrying and civil engineering for nearly 200 years, to power drills, pile-drivers, underground rock loaders and a host of other tools. On the far left is a typical four-wheeled unit common from the early years of the 20th century until the 1970s. Then the two-wheeled type became usual — the one on the right is a Broom-Wade two-tool machine. Very large machines are represented here by the Ingersol-Rand Whisperflow 480-SL.
Studio 509

Main picture: To prepare for major blasting of rock overburden at mines, large self-propelled crawler-mounted blast-hole drills are a standard feature. This Bucyrus 39R diesel-hydraulic-powered machine can punch holes between 9ft and 12ft 3in diameter to a depth of 35ft in a single pass. This one is working at a Western USA copper mine.

Cranes

Below: This Marion 35-M self-propelled mobile lattice-boom crane is one of a complete range of contractor size cranes and excavators made by the Marion Power Shovel Co until the 1960s, when production ceased in favour of large mining draglines, shovels and blast-hole drills. This particular machine is a useful crane to have at this heavy engineering stockyard (perhaps Marion's own factory in Ohio during the late 1960s). Marion is now an integral part of its one-time great rival, Bucyrus International of Milwaukee, Wisconsin.

Left: The AR-600E Tadano eight-wheel hydraulic telescopic truck-mounted crane. Cranes in this series are similar to hundreds working on construction projects all over the world with capacities at the top end ranging to several hundred tons. When disaster strikes, the mobile crane is often the first on the scene in the wake of the emergency services. Rail, bus, plane or truck crashes, collapsed bridges, bombed buildings, earthquake-damaged buildings and Grand Prix racing circuits worldwide show off the capabilities of the fast-travelling, fast-acting, totally-mobile hydraulic crane. Manufacturer Tadano of Japan has now joined forces with Faun of Germany.

Below: The AC-650 from Mannesmann-Dematic is claimed to be the most powerful telescopic crane in the world which can travel the highway with its boom on board. Its capacity is a huge 650 tons: mounted on nine axles with lattice fly jib, it can achieve heights of 139.5m. *Mannesmann-Dematic AG, Zweibrücken*

Left: When the Demag CC12000 crawler lattice-boom crane was first announced in the mid-1990s, its size and capability were startling. Lifting capacity of 1,000 tons made it the world's largest fully-slewing crawler crane. Now an even larger Demag crane has begun work. The CC12000 Superlifter has lifted a five-storey steel building (weighing over 900 tons) onto an oil platform, among many other heavy lifts. *Mannesmann-Dematic AG, Zweibrücken*

Right: The Demag CC12600 crawler crane (with the red and white boom) can lift 1,600 tons at a radius of 12m. Various boom configurations are available to a maximum of 138m for the main boom, or 198m with a boom extension. *Van Seumeren, Holland BV & Mannesmann-Dematic*

Far right: Massive crawler cranes, sometimes equipped with specially designed 'ringer' devices, are used to assist heavy lifts for moving and installing gigantic engineering structures for the petroleum, nuclear, off-shore gas and oil industries, and also for the transportation and erection of large container cranes, coal unloading devices or other heavy engineering applications. Transporters with dozens of axles and hundreds of wheels often have high-tonnage hydraulic-jack lifting systems throughout, enabling them to move and partially install truly mammoth objects weighing hundreds or even thousands of tons. Around the world, specialist lifting and transportation companies such as Van Seumeran and Mammoet are able to handle some of the largest man-made engineered structures, based on years of experience. With the use of ultra-modern computer planning programmes, they are able to install ready-constructed vessels which would otherwise require to be made, disassembled, transported and reconstructed on the site. Engineering and lifting specialists from Belgium, the Netherlands and Germany are amongst the world leaders.

A massive Manitowoc M1200-R with its patented 'ringer' attachment being assisted by another large Manitowoc heavy-duty crawler crane, works in Singapore to erect this mighty pressure vessel. Such vessels often weigh from around 450 to well over 1,000 tons. *Mammoet*

Left: The roof of the 1.2km-long passenger terminal complex of the new Chek Lap Kok Airport, Hong Kong was assembled from modular components. Walter Wright-Mammoet handled the transport and lifting of a total of 129 roof modules using Demag lattice-boom crawler cranes, models CC2600, CC4000 and CC4800 (the model nearest the camera). *Mammoet*

Below: A vast pressure vessel weighing well over 1,000 tons is transported on a Mammoet special purpose trailer: individual hydraulic cylinders compensate for deformities in the ground on which it is moving. *Mammoet*

The largest mobile crane ever to see service in the United Kingdom was delivered to Ainscough Crane Hire Ltd of Wigan in 1998. The eight-axle Liebherr (model LTM 11000 DS/LGD 1550) can lift a maximum of 1,000 tons and features a unique twin-boom: in part a conventional strut jib, it has a telescopic system which cuts in half the time taken to erect and dismantle the boom for operations compared to conventional booms. The lattice system permits greater lifting capacities to be handled at maximum radius. Known as the 'Millennium Lifter', it cost £3.2 million, and travels with 24 wagons to carry its ballast and counter-weights.

The photograph shows the crane at work on a contract for Devonport Engineering Consortium Ltd, Plymouth, lifting a newly-fabricated trawler weighing approximately 210 tons. The crane was rigged with 42m main SLBB boom, 160 tons of crane counter-weight, and 190-ton suspended derrick counter-weight. *Ainscough Crane Hire Ltd*